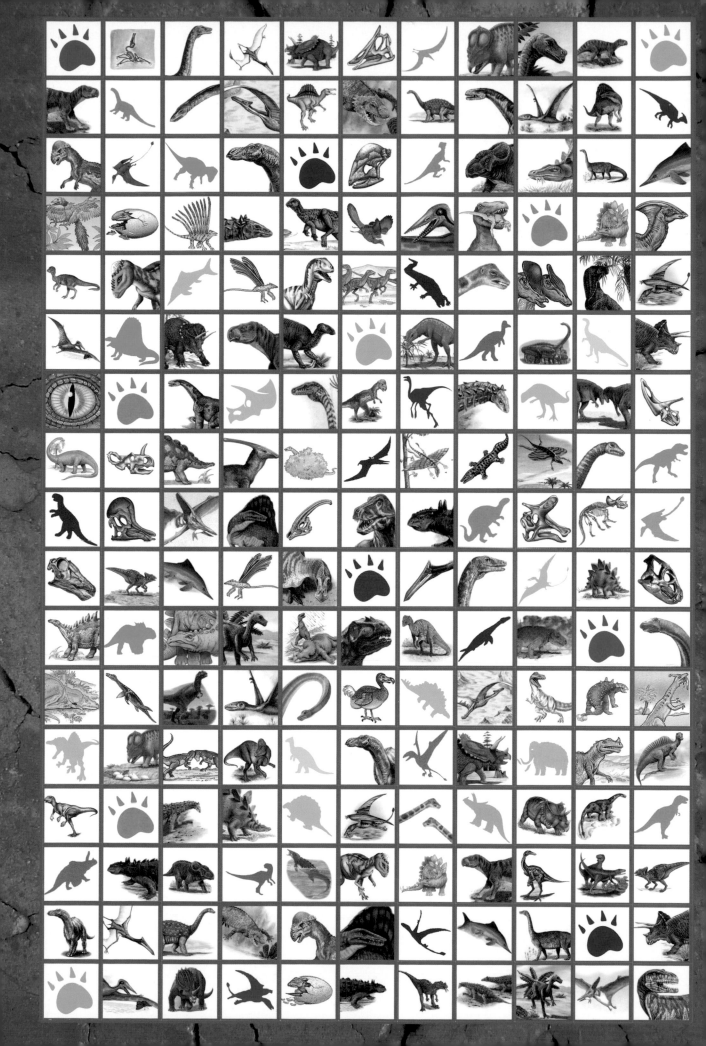

TYRANNOSAURUS REX

STEGOSAURUS

TRICERATOPS

VELOCIRAPTOR

DIPLODOCUS

BRACHIOSAURUS

IGUANODON

TRICERATOPS

TROODON

DINOSAUR

DINOSAUR

T-REX

DINOSAUR

STICKER BURST

www.alligatorbooks.co.uk

The Alligator logo is a registered
trademark of Alligator Products Ltd.

© 2021 Alligator Products Ltd.
Published in 2021 by Alligator Products Ltd.
2nd Floor, 314 Regents Park Road,
London N3 2JX.

Printed in China.1828

Colour in this picture of the
TYRANNOSAURUS REX.

COLOUR KEY

1 grey
2 blue
3 brown
4 orange
5 yellow
6 green

Colour in the picture using the colour key.

DINO JOKE!

Q: What should you do if you find a dinosaur in your bed?
A: Find somewhere else to sleep!

WHAT IS HIDING?

Colour the shapes with a dot in them to discover what is hiding in the picture.

Draw a dinosaur that flies, in the space below and colour it in.

IDENTICAL DINOSAURS

Which two dinosaurs are the same? Circle them.

B.

D.

A.

C.

E.

Answer: B and C

ODD ONE OUT

Draw a circle around the image which is the odd one out in each line.

A.

1. 2. 3. 4. 5. 6. 7.

B.

1. 2. 3. 4. 5. 6.

C.
1. 2. 3. 4. 5.

5

Answer: A = 1, B = 4, C = 2

How many GIGANOTOSAURUSES can you count below?

Count carefully.

Answer: 12

What did the ZEPHYROSAURUS eat?
Follow the lines to find out whether they ate plants, meat or both!

PLANTS

MEAT

Answer: Plants

This dinosaur is missing his head!
Join the dots to finish the picture.

DINOSAUR FACT FILE

Invent your own dinosaur and write in this fact file:

Dinosaur name: _____

Likes to eat: _____

Does it have spikes? _____

Can it fly? _____

Can it swim? _____

How tall is it? Taller than a house? _____

Draw a picture of your dinosaur below.

8

Help the PTERANODON fly back through the cloud maze.

START

FINISH

Trace over and colour this picture.

DINO FACT!

The Pteranodon was a flying reptile that lived during the time of the dinosaurs – it was not a dinosaur, but was a close relative of the dinosaurs.

9

Nobody really knows what colours
dinosaurs were, so let your
imagination run wild and colour
this dinosaur in the
brightest colours you have!

How many trilobites can
you see? Count carefully.

Answer: 10

10

Colour in the picture using the colour key:

COLOUR KEY

1 grey   4 orange
2 blue   5 yellow
3 brown   6 green

SPOT THE DIFFERENCE

Can you spot five differences between these pictures?

DINO JOKE

Q: Which dinosaur slept all day?
A: Tri-snore-atops!

28

WHAT IS HIDING?

Colour the shapes with a dot in them to discover what is hiding in the picture.

Draw your own picture of a Tyrannosaurus rex in the box and colour it in.

13

Finish the second picture to make the two SPINOSAURUSES look exactly the same.

JOIN THE DOTS
to reveal the hidden dinosaur!

23 24

25

22

21

20

14

13   12

11

19   15

16

17

18

1

2

3

10

4

9   5

6

8   7

14

Colour in this picture of the
TYRANNOSAURUS REX.

DINO JOKE!

Q: What do you
get when dinosaurs
crash their cars?
A: Tyrannosaurus
wrecks!

15

ODD ONE OUT

Draw a circle around the image which is the odd one out in each line.

A. 1. 2. 3. 4. 5.

B. 1. 2. 3. 4. 5.

C. 1. 2. 3. 4. 5. 6. 7.

D. 1. 2. 3. 4. 5. 6.

Answer: A = 2, B = 3, C =1, D = 6

How many skeletons can you count?

Look very carefully!

Answer: 11

16

WORDSEARCH

Can you find these words hidden in the wordsearch? Draw a circle around the words you find. Tick them off as you go.

Fossil ☐
Extinct ☐
Teeth ☐
Claw ☐
Plates ☐
Spikes ☐
Bones ☐
Horns ☐

```
C V T P W Y U A S T O P
Y B D L S W Q N E M K L
X O E A X K E A X G H D
H N B T X T E E T H O N
J E R E Z B N U I W R J
D S U S X Z J W N M N C
A I U P V W E O C X S O
F O S S I L U E T S A M
P V B X T U E C N P R H
W S P I K E S E K R X C
T E I C L A W X N O I E
B Y R W Y T N B M I O U
```

Draw a circle round the piece of jigsaw that completes this picture.

a

b

c

If you discovered a new dinosaur what would you call it?

....

If your dinosaur looks like a lizard remember to end its name with 'saurus' (saurus is Greek for lizard).

DINO JOKE!

Q: Who makes the best prehistoric reptile clothes?
A: A dino-sewer!

18

CREATE YOUR OWN DINOSAUR

Make it as colourful as possible.

Copy this picture of a TROODON using the grid to help.

DINO FACT!

The Troodon's cat-like eyes helped it hunt at night. They had very large brains and were very intelligent.

CROSSWORD

Solve the crossword by answering the questions to fill in the missing spaces.

1   A Tyrannosaurus likes to eat ....?

2   A Triceratops has how many horns?

3   Complete the name of this dinosaur, Tyrannosaurus ...?

Trace over half of the dinosaur to finish the picture.

Answers:
1. meat
2. three
3. rex

Colour in this picture of these GALLODACTYLUS.

Cross out every other letter, starting with 'r' to reveal the name of the dinosaur above!

rasleavmaogsgauuyrbuws

Answer: Alamosaurus

Decorate these dinosaur footprints with colourful patterns and designs.

This **GIGANOTOSAURUS** has had 3 babies. Can you draw one and then colour it in?

DINOSAUR DICE GAME

Each player chooses a dinosaur then throws a dice. Whichever number comes up, colour in that numbered square in your dinosaur's column and see who gets to the finish line first.

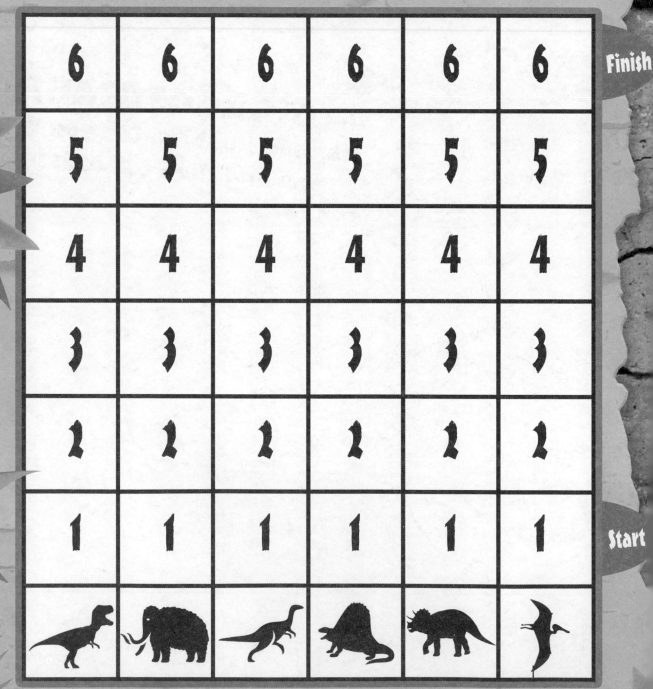

Finish

Start

14

COLOUR IN

these three vegetarian prehistoric dinosaurs!

DINO FACT!
Most dinosaurs were vegetarian!

Which path will lead the dinosaur to the egg?

1.

2.

3.

Draw lines to match each dinosaur with the correct description.

A. I have a long neck and like to eat from trees.

1.

B. I have plates on my back.

2.

C. I can swim underwater.

3.

Colour in the area with a dot to reveal the picture!

MIRROR MESSAGE!

This dinosaur is holding a message that can only be read in a mirror. Can you read what it says?

Dinosaurs were alive for over 1 million years.

17

Copy this picture of a
DIPLODOCUS!

Use the grid to help.
Then colour it in.

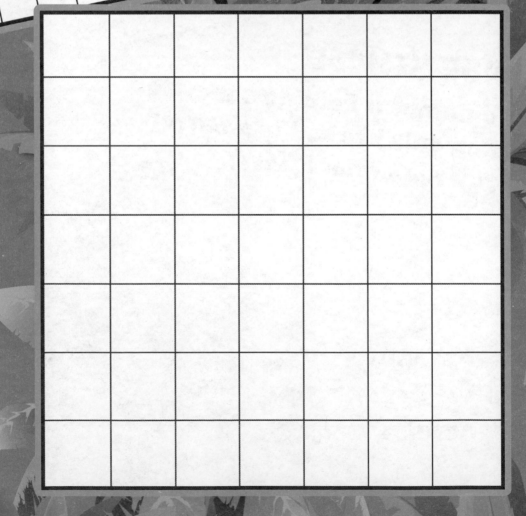

Join the dots to finish this picture of a
PLATEOSAURUS.

DINO JOKE!

Q: What type of tool does a prehistoric reptile carpenter use?
A: A dino-saw!

Draw the missing horn on this Triceratops, then colour it in using any colour you like.

19

HIDDEN WORD

Each dinosaur footprint below has a letter on it. Colour in all the footprints that have letters belonging to the name of a mountain that erupts with hot lava!

DINO FACT!

Tyrannosaurus rex means 'tyrant lizard'

Answer: volcano

30

Use the key below to colour in the picture.

How many bones can you count hidden on this page?

Answer: 5

COLOUR KEY

1 orange
2 red
3 green
4 blue
5 brown
6 yellow

31

Colour in these dinosaurs using only pink, yellow and orange!

Do you know the name of the dinosaur below?

Cross out every other letter, starting with 't' to reveal the name!

vtexlboncmilrkahpytqoar

Use the chart below to decode an amazing fact!

a b c d e f g h i j k l m
1 2 3 4 5 6 7 8 9 10 11 12 13

n o p q r s t u v w x y z
14 15 16 17 18 19 20 21 22 23 24 25 26

3 15 18 25 20 8 15 19 1 21 18 21 19

_____

13 5 1 14 19   8 5 12 13 5 20

_____   _____

12 9 26 1 18 4

_____

Answer: corythosaurus means helmet lizard

Colour in this
CORYTHOSAURUS.

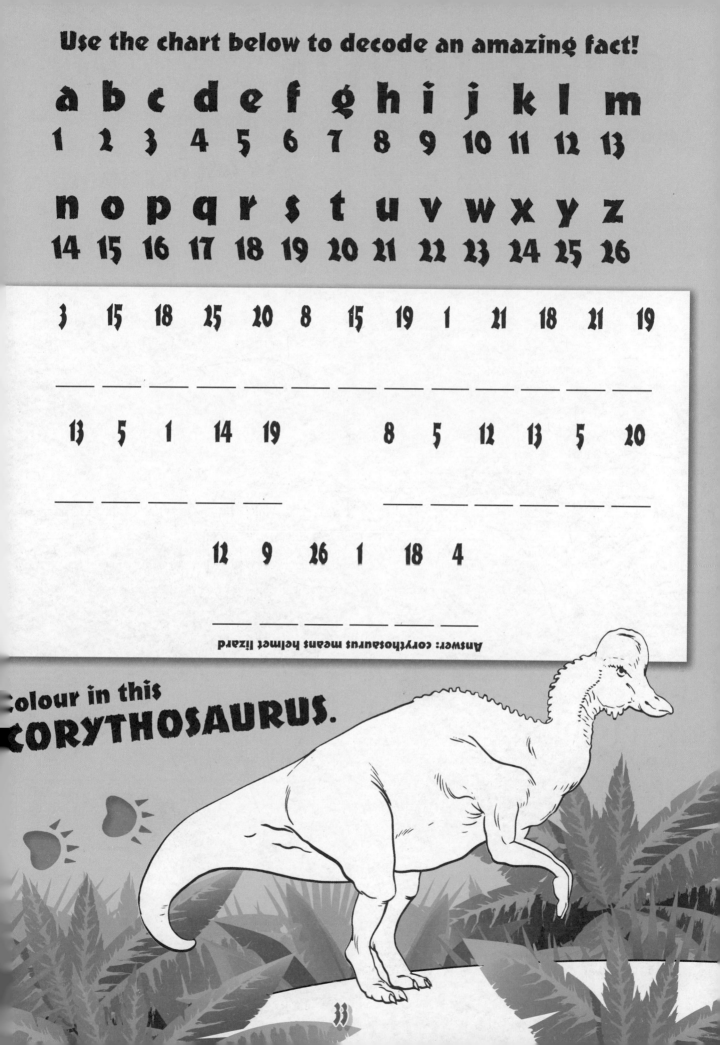

33

COLOUR THEM IN

Colour each of the dinosaurs in the picture.

Use lots of colours.

DINO JOKE!

Q: What do you get when a dinosaur blows its nose?
A: OUT of the way!

WHAT IS HIDING?

Colour in each piece with a dot on it to reveal the hidden surprise!

Let your imagination run wild and colour this Velociraptor in the brightest colours you have!

Colour the
TRICERATOPS

USE GREEN, BROWN AND YELLOW.

DINO JOKE!

Q: What do you call a dinosaur that never gives up?
A: Try and try and try and try-ceratops

...or any colour you choose. No-one knows what colours the dinosaurs were!

36

Can you make the **STEGOSAURUS** below look like the one on the right? Draw the missing bits to make these two dinosaurs the same!

DINO FACT!
The Stegosaurus weighed about 4 tons, but its brain was about the size of a dog's!

DINO FACT!
Did you know that the name Stegosaurus means 'covered lizard'?

NAME THIS DINOSAUR

When you think you know the answer hold this book up to the mirror to reveal the correct answer.

DIPLODOCUS

Now colour it in!

How many dinosaurs can you count on the right? Look closely!

Help the QUETZALCOATLUS fly through the maze to land.

START

FINISH

Colour in this dinosaur.

SPOT THE DIFFERENCE

Can you see 5 differences between the pictures? Circle all the differences in the bottom picture.

Answer: 1 = the Raptor's right claw has disappeared. 2 = The distant tree has gone. 3 = The flying dinosaur has flown away. 4 = The Raptor's eye has turned red. 5 = The leaves have blown away.

Copy the **T-REX** using the grid to help you.

Draw a picture of any dinosaur whose name begins with the letter T!

ODD ONE OUT

In each line there is one different dinosaur. Circle the odd one out.

Look very carefully!

Answer: A = 1, B = 3, C = 1, D = 6, E = 5

WORDSEARCH

See if you can find all these dinosaurs in the puzzle below. Tick them off as you go.

```
P L I O S A U R U S V B G
A Y I P W C J L Z B D J I
R Z K X M D Y P K H I C G
A J R M X P L O K S M S A
S U C H O M I M U S O M N
A U Y S A U R E A P R V O
U Y Q V B M X S J I P K T
R U L M H Y Y R C N H R O
O Y O B E G R K S O O S S
L D W Y N H K C R S D C A
O N Q U O J F K S A O S U
P X N P D L G H C U N K R
H J B W U O H R S R T S U
U U K S S W U S G U K C S
S D L Z V B Y D R S P V C
```

Suchomimus ☐

Giganotosaurus ☐

Spinosaurus ☐

Parasaurolophus ☐

Dimorphodon ☐

Pliosaurus ☐

Henodus ☐

DINO JOKE!

Q: How do you invite a dinosaur to a cafe?
A: Tea, Rex?

43

DINOSAUR MATHS

Work out the answers to the sums and write the answers in the boxes.

A.

X =

B.

+ =

C.

+ =

D.

X =

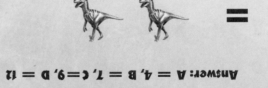

Answer: A = 4, B = 7, c = 9, D = 12

MEMORY GAME

Look at this list of dinosaur names below then close the book and see how many you can remember!

Henodus   Dimorphodon

Pliosaurus   Spinosaurus

Parasaurolophus   Giganotosaurus

Copy this picture of a
DIMORPHODON
so that it has a twin!

Find which dinosaurs match and then colour the matching pair in.

45

Invent a dinosaur that can FLY! Draw and colour in the brand new dinosaur that you have created.

Tip: Think about what it might look like. Would it have a beak like a bird or padded beak like a duck?

ODD ONE OUT

Which of these dinosaurs is different? Draw a circle around it.

B.

F.

A.

D.

C.

E.

Answer: D

46

Colour the
HERRERASAURUS.

DINO FACT!

The name literally means 'Herrera's lizard' and was a bipedal carnivore that was approximately 20 feet long, 3 feet high at the hip and probably weighed around 700 pounds.

How many skulls can you count?
Write the answer.

DINO JOKE!

Q: What do you call a blind dinosaur?
A: Do-ya-think he-saurus.

Answer: 9

This
CERTIFICATE
is awarded to

_____

for being

TOTALLY DINOSAUR MAD!!

48